D1592794

From Klecko, the Midwest Book Award-winning author of "Hitman-Baker-Casketmaker: Aftermath of an American's Clash with ICE" and "Lincolnland."

"3 a.m. Austin Texas" is the story of a boy who threw away his life only to reclaim it while hitchhiking across America in the dead of winter.

Richard O'hara
Thanks for everything
Klecko

TEXSS
63 of 100
KLECK

3 a.m. Austin Texas

3 A.M.

AUSTIN

TEXAS

Boy On The Run

By KLECKO

PARIS MORNING
PUBLICATIONS

Published in 2021 by Paris Morning Publications
parismorningpublications.com

Published and printed in the United States of America
ISBN: 978-0-578-95706-7

Cover design by Audrey Campbell
ataudrey.com

Other books by Klecko

Lincolnland

*Hitman-Baker-Casketmaker: Aftermath of an
    American's Clash with ICE*

Out for a Lark

The Bluebeard of Happiness

A Pox Upon Your Blessings

Houdini in St. Paul

My British Hindu Bible

Robert Bly and the Monk in His Cell

Mayor 4 Life

Brando Land

Dedicated to

The Librarians of District #281 in Minneapolis
For looking out for me
For not making me talk
Thank you for introducing me
To Brenda Ueland
Collectively, I'm pretty sure
You saved me

Eternally in your debt,
Klecko

Based on a True Story
1982

POP BOTTLE LADY

The final year I attended school . . .
At my bus stop, there were no girls
It was a place where testosterone and anger
Mingled with cigarette smoke and uncertainty
During my final year, pop bottles were made of glass
Most days somebody would bring Pepsi to be shared
Thug decorum dictated, whoever killed the bottle
Had to smash it in the street
Each time we did this, a woman brought out a broom
And dustpan to clean up our mess
Every day, every day, every day
While we sat perched in the back of the bus
She issued a non-judgmental glance
Indicating she was prepared
To repeat the routine the following day
Before long, my friends became ashamed and stopped
But I continued
I didn't know how to surrender
And therefore, remained an irritant
Until the school year ended

COIN OF THE REALM

On the table, in the middle
An enormous bundle of cash
We waited patiently
Eyes bugged out, necks corded with tension
We waited patiently
For the kingpin to peel off our shares
And send us on our way
In the movies, fellow grifters almost always disclose
How they're going to spend their windfall
I kept my mouth shut
Smart enough to realize
I was stupid enough to believe
A similar success was likely

ON THE ROAD

Once you've made something disappear
There will always be brighter people
Who don't have to find what disappeared
They just have to connect you to it
Such was my plight
At a moment short of panic
My mother's second husband told me
If a person doesn't have resources, they can't negotiate
Then he asked if I had resources
I said no, so he pulled out his wallet
And handed me five twenties
A gesture unfamiliar at our house
Then he drove me to the Hwy. 35 on-ramp and explained
Problematic situations have a tendency to be forgotten
When the dumb ass who started them, stays far away
Then he smiled and tossed me my duffle
As the man on the radio announced
We were experiencing the coldest January of the decade

INTERSTATE I-35

Constructed in 1956
Starts in Duluth, Minnesota
Ends in Laredo, Texas
Length 1,569.06 miles
States – Minnesota, Iowa, Missouri, Kansas, Oklahoma, Texas
Major Cities – Minneapolis-St. Paul, Des Moines, Kansas City,
Wichita, Oklahoma City, Dallas-Fort Worth, Austin
9th longest interstate highway
3rd longest North-South highway

HAIRCUT IN DUBUQUE

On the day of my exodus, rides were few and far between
I began to get discouraged
I wondered if I'd make it out of Minnesota by nightfall
My mother's second husband explained
Hitchhiking maintained absolute rules
Rule #1 was important, if I wanted to have success
I needed to smell better than the driver at all times
Rule #2 stated, keep your hair short
It should never touch your ears or collar
I had a mullet
When I eventually crossed the state line
I was frozen and decided to trade vanity for acceptance
As I walked up to a barber shop in Dubuque
They said they were closing up
One of the barbers looked at my duffle
Then he looked at me and asked where I was heading
I told him I didn't know
But I didn't want to arrive there looking like this
And for the first time since getting myself into trouble
I felt ashamed
I gulped, my eyes got watery
And the old buck smiled and sat me in his chair
And gave me my first crew cut since fourth grade

ROGER & ME

At a point when my toes were so frozen
Amputation would have been welcome
A man driving a van full of young women
Pulled over and offered me the shotgun seat
He introduced himself as Roger
The chauffeur of talented caricature artists
He asked where I was going
I didn't know, and answered Kansas City
He asked what I was going to do there
I didn't know and told him so
Roger lit up a smoke, turned to the girls
Then back to me and said
It's good to have a secret, something to defend
Then he explained the caricature crew
Was setting camp in Des Moines for the night
And I should consider partying with them
I asked what was so special about Des Moines
Roger asked if I ever read Kerouac
I nodded no, and the girls rolled their eyes
As Roger explained that Kerouac wrote
The prettiest girls in the world lived in Des Moines
Within the first 100 pages of ON THE ROAD
It was at this moment
I decided Kansas City could wait

MUSINGS FROM THE ON-RAMP

During a moment I was certain God hated me
I kept my arm extended, thumb pointing up
Zoom-Zoom, cars whizzed by
Zoom-Zoom, nobody stopped
During the moment I slept under my first bridge
I comforted myself by remembering
I was kind of like the Christ
When he had no place to call home
Nowhere to lay his head
And then I smiled
Until I frowned
Remembering just how
Things worked out for him

BALLS

The night before I went on the road
Mother's second husband entered my room
With a plastic bag, and parting advice
The bag contained two balls
One was made of hard red rubber
It was meant to keep me company when I was lonely
The second was a yellow Nerf football
It was meant to be used, in the event I made a friend

WHEEL OF FORTUNE

They have their reasons
Why they pull over
Why they pick you up
Their reasons vary
What they really want
Is almost always
One of the following
Save you
Scare you
Sex you
Or sleep
While you take the wheel
Such was the case
When Horace
From Norris (South Dakota)
Handed me a map of Iowa
And told me
To get him to the "X"
While he passed out
On the back seat

SHOWDOWN WITH THE AMISH

It was six below zero
I was surprised
How slippery dirt roads could become
I pulled into an intersection
Wanting to turn left
But, across the highway
Was an Amish woman in a buggy
She had the right of way
For reasons unknown
She refused to cross
So, I too sat motionless, idling
While the two of us engaged
In a quiet dialogue consisting of stares
And a flashing blinker
Columns of steam rose from the horse's nostrils
And I began to realize
If an agreement wasn't negotiated
She'd crush me with patience
And simply wait for my gas tank to run dry

DE SOTO IOWA

Because vampires keep me awake
With their chronic complaints
Let's drive tonight
Because you ally with darkness
I'll close my eyes while you take the wheel
Let's drive tonight
Because California would be predictable
Fate might choose De Soto Iowa
The birthplace of John Wayne
Nowhere is further from civilization
And when we get there, with nothing to do
We should drink red wine in a parking lot
Distracting ourselves with the kind of conversation
You only have sitting on the world's sidelines
And if we should stay awake
Until the moment the sun begins to rise
Maybe you could let me know
What life has planned for me

PASSING THROUGH COUNCIL BLUFFS

Her name was Terri, her car was messy
Her face was pretty, the windshield frosted
She asked where I was headed, I mentioned Kansas City
She offered an alternative, let's go to the movies
Driving, drifting, flirting, sitting
It appeared we liked each other, just because
We saw the movie Scanners, it must have been romantic
Because when the villains employed telekinesis
And people's heads blew up
Terri squeezed my hand with a level of pressure
That announced I might be trusted
When the movie was over
We retreated to the parking lot
Where she offered me to come home with her
I paused
For the first time in a long time
I felt good
Until I remembered I had nothing to offer
Causing me to grab my duffle
And walk into the night

LAWRENCE KANSAS

William might be the first William
I ever met
Who actually insisted on being called William
Once that was established, he pulled into a diner
Where he bought us dinner
And spoke to me about hippy courses
He taught at KU
When our meal was finished, we went into the kitchen
Where we picked up boxes of produce
We would deliver to his wife
She worked at a health food store
Which I never got to see
Because I was guilty of not knowing
It was poor form to criticize John Lennon
When the Beatles were on the radio
As I did this, William pulled over
Handing me bananas for my effort
While informing me
I was a generous witness
But it was in everyone's best interest
If we parted ways

BIRDS OVER KANSAS

Ice and asphalt, warmth a distant memory
I convinced myself, I wasn't lonely
Wondering when I could return home
Nothing in Kansas, is worse than nothing in Iowa
Because in Kansas, it isn't intentional
I convinced myself, I wasn't lonely
Without lifting a finger, I lifted my eyes
Without recognizing the species, or the song
A flock of birds flew past, and it occurred to me
They had to be gods or aliens
Their purpose, beyond determined
Certainly, a superior species
In the city, like angels, their deeds go unnoticed
As if their feathers were transparent
As if they even cared
That once again
Their mandate will be disobeyed by fools

MEALS - 1

Days ago, loneliness encroached
Speaking in whispers
Assuring me
She was beyond formidable
The nastiest antagonist
One could meet
I believed her
Until two days later
When I met hunger

MEALS - 2

You never know it
Until it's too late
How important food is
It's necessary
It was necessary
But funds were lacking
There was zero room for error
When balancing
Calories and currency
I recalled advice
From an earlier ride
A soldier, who hitched across Europe
He said . . .
Protein in winter
Electrolytes in summer
I popped into my sleeping bag
Turtle in a shell
With the understanding
At daybreak
I would find protein

MEALS - 3

Hours before daybreak
Hunger woke me
Forced me to walk miles
Finally . . .
An all-night convenience store
A loaf of Wonder Bread
A jar of Skippy
My stomach made noises
As I retreated in darkness
Knowing soon
I would make breakfast
Underneath the bridge
Considering options
Before the sun came up
Drinking water
While doing my best
Not to think of milk

MEALS - 4

24 slices
Enough for 12 sandwiches
After double checking
To make sure nobody was around
I laid the slices out neatly
On top of my sleeping bag
Four across, six down
I didn't have a knife
Just some folded cardboard
After applying the peanut butter
I assembled sandwiches
Eating one, stacking eleven
Returning the surplus
To its plastic bag
Jewels in a vault
Hunger was defeated
If only for the moment
As the sun began to surface
Loneliness encroached
Speaking in whispers

COFFEE KLATCH AT THE LEE SUMMIT CAFÉ

They appeared to be regulars
Sitting at banquet tables in the back
The women wore plastic rain scarves
Most of which were floral
The men, ball caps advertising tractors
Or battleships they served on
While the women chirped
And the men mumbled
The waitress saw me and my duffle
Leaning against the counter
And motioned for me to join them
Before she took my order
She looked at my duffle
And asked where I was headed
I answered Texas
The room became silent
Until I asked, if something was wrong with Texas
The waitress shook her head no
But reminded me
I'd have to pass through Oklahoma
Causing them to place their hands on me
And pray for my safety

KANSAS CITY TONY

Kansas City Tony, told me he was lonely
A statement that unnerved me, as he smiled
He spoke of his vocation
Selling commercial bathroom supplies
His joy was illustrated with statistics
20% of men won't wash their hands
40% who do, won't wash long enough
50% won't even use soap
The topic disturbed me enough to remain silent
But the joy wasn't exhausted, so Tony continued
When you shit in a public restroom
Shit in the first stall, it's always the cleanest
People skip it for privacy
At this moment, I decided to hate Kansas City Tony
I hated him as he pulled off the freeway
I hated him as he pulled into the gas station
Where he mentioned he'd only be a minute
And asked if there was anything I needed
When I shook my head no, he stared at his keys
And let me know he'd leave them in the ignition
So I would remain warm
That's when it occurred to me
Kansas City Tony was my friend

WHEEL OF FORTUNE - 2

Car pulls over, door opens
Safety is determined by a momentary assessment
Perspective is often influenced
By just how frozen your feet are
Dude with the yellow bandana
He's not right, I can't say why
But he isn't
If I get in, there's a 14% chance
Tomorrow, I'll wake up
Padlocked in a cage
But my feet are frozen
That's the problem with intuition
It tends to lean on the minority fraction
Forgetting there's an 86% chance
This guy's alright
Who knows
He might even buy breakfast

A NEW KIND OF CAMELOT

On a day that neither both
Or none of my boots were missing
One was
On a day I was in need of a small victory
The universe made it apparent
God was against everyone
On a day the sun had only been up two hours
I surrendered
And crawled back into my sleeping bag
Sinking my hand into the duffle
Bypassing breakfast and a Bible
To produce the only thing that offered hope
A map of Texas
Abilene, Austin
Dallas, Denton
San Antonio and Houston
Whispered invitations as the frost bit hard
I fell back asleep
Only to be visited in a dream
By a cowboy angel
Who announced
Everything would end up making sense
If I could just find my way to Corpus Christi
And discover the value
In learning to take a punch

EPISTLE TO THE PEOPLE OF WICHITA

It wasn't one, or some: every face recoiled
The moment I entered Wichita
My chilly reception
Was connected to a wardrobe mishap
My left foot sported a size 15 Army boot
My right foot was wrapped in burlap
Tied snug with a cord
Money was tight
I tried to purchase a single replacement boot
Shoe-Guy answered no
So . . .
I ended up buying both boots
I ended up spending half my bankroll
Later that afternoon I sat in a parking lot
Reading my Bible, reading John Chapter 12
Where Christ decides to enter Jerusalem
On the back of an ass
Hoping people would consider him humble
It's not often I correct a Messiah
But I'm pretty sure he'd be more humble
If he entered Jerusalem
With a foot wrapped in burlap
Tied snug with a cord

MOCKINGBIRD

In a world where sore throats
Wet socks and bruises, fail to merit mention
Independence arrives, constructed slowly
With redundancy and grit
Makeshift and temporary
Typically constructed by pioneers who lack
Resources and belief in themselves
This is my understanding
Because this was my plight
Until the morning, I woke up in Oklahoma
Sprawled out on the pavement
With the notion concrete was becoming softer
Sprawled out on the pavement
Motionless, flat on my back
I began to smile
I did believe in things
Things I couldn't articulate
Things on the tip of my tongue
Understanding truth starts by understanding purpose
And understanding purpose became second nature
The moment I realized
I believed in things
I didn't have names for

OUTSIDE OF BLACKWELL OKLAHOMA

A rusted Impala pulled over
I rode shotgun, the sedan was occupied
Three Apaches, and the tools they used
For restoring barns across the panhandle
On the back floor, a body lay motionless
White matted hair across his face
Questions weren't asked
Marlboros were passed around
Everybody smoked, visibility was limited
Car too fast, wind too cold
We couldn't crack the windows
Finally, the body stirred, moaned
Rolled to one side
After emptying his bladder
On the car floor, he announced
I am Johnny Loud Thunder
My sons are taking me to Texas
So I can depart from this world
From the place I entered
When it was time to separate
I was offered well wishes and cigarettes
Johnny Loud Thunder smiled weakly
Then chanted a final blessing
Before I returned to the highway
To process the gifts I'd been given

TRUCK STOP / OKLAHOMA CITY

A part of the world exists
But goes unseen
A space of transition
A place people drive through
Thinking of where they were
Or where they were going
In truth, not far off
From an Oklahoma truck stop
I wondered if anybody missed me
I wondered if anybody cared
I wanted to call home
I wanted to speak to mother
But, I wasn't sure
How much strength remained in her heart
I wanted to call home
Or anywhere
But there was nothing to say
So I considered against it

PARKING LOT

Pit stop or oasis
Predicated by circumstance
To everyone who entered
This Oklahoma truck stop
I was the rookie
A focal point for regulars
Caught in the crosshairs of
Truckers, travelers, Bible bangers
And lot lizards
Perched on my duffle
I sat out of sight
Unsuccessfully
A spot of weather rolled in
A car door opened, she offered shelter
I hopped in
She offered anything I needed
I misread the cue
And asked for milk
To which she replied
I do believe you are serious
Aren't you precious?

TRUCK STOP / OKLAHOMA CITY

People came, people went
Days passed, I stayed
People were nice to me
Soft-hearted truckers were overly generous
By overpaying me
To sweep out their semi-trailers
Soft-hearted truckers were overly generous
And offered me companionship
And ways to kill time
A guy with a name starting with "H"
Told me I could take one book
From a box of dozens
Books like . . .
THE SEA WOLF by Jack London
THE GREAT GATSBY by F. Scott Fitzgerald
RUMBLE FISH by S.E. Hinton
And THE EXECUTIONER'S SONG by Norman Mailer
I went with RUMBLE FISH

BOOK REPORT

The rumbles stopped in Tulsa
About the time dope became popular
Those who liked to fight, had no course to follow
Rusty-James wanted to bring thuggery back
He was the younger brother of The Motorcycle Boy
Motorcycle Boy was the former gang president
On the run, royalty in exile
But when he returns . . .
He and Rusty-James have to make decisions
The book is slight, but heavy and artful
At a time in my life when things were volatile
It was helpful to consider
Breaking away from a hopeless routine
Might be my only chance

SILENT NIGHT – LONELY NIGHT

Things were starting to get just a bit too comfortable
At the Oklahoma City truck stop
Should I stay, or should I go
The sun was about to go down
Things were starting to become static
Texas was calling
What was I waiting for
The sun went down
A guy named Skipper
Who drove a Mack
Served as an epiphany, by offering up
Leftover French fries, and an opportunity
To hitch a ride to Denton, in several hours
At one a.m.
I said yes before thinking
He hopped in his cab and slept
I sat perched on my duffle
Looking for somebody to say goodbye to
Nobody I knew passed by, which made me sad
So I pulled out my Bible
And tried to memorize the books
In chronological order

TRIBUTE

After crossing the state line
I felt recharged
Texas is the most confident place on earth
New York's not close
And California can't touch
The Lone Star State's
Energy, success and grit . . .
Somewhere in Denton
I hopped out of Skipper's truck
And stood on the road's shoulder
I smiled, and began unpeeling layers
Like King David
Dancing before the Lord in Jerusalem
Jackets, hoodies, stocking cap
Stripped, swung, and tossed to the ditch
I was thankful, I was happy
Few things refresh a pioneer
Like a lightened load

NORTH TEXAS STATE

The team's nickname is Mean Green
In tribute to the Pittsburgh Steelers'
Defensive tackle, anchor of the Steel Curtain
Winner of four Super Bowls
Their stadium was basic
Not much bigger than a high school's
Security measures were minimal
Hop a fence, cross a field
Sit alone, sit on the bleachers
I did, while enjoying a Pepsi
I withdrew the yellow Nerf football
With the hope I would make a friend
And have a catch
Nobody came, I daydreamed
I remembered the commercial
Where some kid gave Joe his Coke
And Joe tossed the kid his jersey
Before disappearing down a tunnel
I remember thinking
If Joe was going to give up
A game-used jersey
He should have held out for Pepsi

NORTH TEXAS STATE - 2

I walked down to the field
Ran with the ball
Football alone is boring
I stood in the middle of the field
Uncertain what to do
So I stood
Until a guy with a big Afro joined me
He ran routes, I threw passes
Only briefly, he didn't speak
After he left
I stood in the middle of the field
Uncertain what to do
I returned to the bleachers
And accidentally kicked over my Pepsi bottle
It shattered against the asphalt
Reminding me of the Pop Bottle Lady
Reminding me of shame
I didn't want to remember those incidents
But I didn't know how to make them go away
So I grabbed my gear
And headed towards Dallas

DENTON TO DALLAS

A car pulls over, he tells her to hop in back
Awarding me the shotgun position
I found the adjustment embarrassing
He seemed to consider the gesture necessary
Her expression, deadpan at best
Supertramp, Breakfast in America played
At a volume that was almost inaudible
SNAP – CRACKLE . . .
She popped bubble wrap with no particular rhythm
He kept talking about nothing
Our conversation, clipped and superficial
SNAP – CRACKLE, SNAP – CRACKLE
I kept talking on the fly
I made things up, I had to say something
I wanted to appear polite
SNAP – CRACKLE . . .
Supertramp, Breakfast in America played
At a volume almost inaudible
Until all I heard was a hush directing me
To a space in my mind
Where ideas weren't shared
I began to remember
That place in Dallas with the watchers

SUMMARY OF YOUTH

Between mother's first and second husband
Patterns developed
Where I was shuffled back and forth
Among relatives, friends, and babysitters
When each of these camps became exhausted
There were unfamiliar people
Who took me into their care
I didn't know how to define my relationship
With these unfamiliar people
In my mind, I thought of them as watchers
Watchers were unpredictable
Some yelled, some hit
But sometimes I got lucky
Like consecutive summers
I was shipped to Dallas
To a house of watchers
Who read my mind
They knew what I wanted
And gave it to me
In abundance

STRIP MALL PARKING LOT

I knew the watchers used to live in Richardson
An affluent suburb of Dallas
But I wasn't sure if they were still there
I hopped into a phone booth
And thumbed through the telephone book
I wasn't sure what to hope for
I wasn't sure if I had enough nerve
To consider reunion
But . . . fear became outweighed
By memories of hope
My finger glanced down columns of names
Zip – Zip – Zip and . . . there they were
I was excited to proceed

A SORT OF HOMECOMING

I rang the bell, the door was answered
Smiles all around
Those who were home called those who weren't
During dinner I was asked why I had come
I explained I was failing life
I explained I was in search of an answer
I explained I was pretty sure
I could find that answer in Texas
Because in Texas
I was loved

INVITATION

The following morning the watchers gathered
Making breakfast amidst squabbles and laughter
It was presented that I consider staying on
A suggestion I quickly interrupted with truth
I have absolutely no idea what I'm doing
But I know there's something wrong with me
You guys have things
In your heads and hearts
But I don't think I do
If I did, they got erased
I don't like being hollow
And I don't know how to fix that
But sometimes when you move to new places
The people you meet don't know you
And you can be something ok
Even if . . .
It's only for a short time

A BIG SEND-OFF

After pancakes
After bacon
The watchers continued tradition
By circling me prior to departure
Circling and chanting...
Wall of Love, Wall of Love
The circle tightened
Tangled
Wall of Love, Wall of Love
They refused to release me
Everyone laughed
Smiles all around

JARRELL - 1

High noon, small town
Fate placed me in Jarrell (Yah-Rell)
Less than an hour from Austin
High noon, small town
A guy in his garage
Working on his car
Looked at me and said
He would shoot me
If I even thought of
Stealing his tools
High noon, small town
I liked this guy
Dude seemed shady
Had grit
I dropped my duffle
Onto the driveway
And stepped into the garage
Explaining . . .

JARRELL – 2

I'm not honest
I'm on the run
Days are hard
You don't get many good moments
But I heard you playing Springsteen
Darkness on the Edge of Town
That's a great album
If you kicked my ass
It would almost be worth it
Mechanic smiles, asks
Need a shower – I say Nah
Hungry – Nah
Need a couple of bucks – Nah, I'm good
But how about milk, you got any milk
Mechanic says chocolate
To which I replied
Even better

JARRELL - 3

Full moon, small town
Laziness kept me in Jarrell
Full moon, small town
Two men's voices, closer to my camp
Than a pioneer would allow
Two men's voices disappeared
Only to be replaced with
The rhythm of slapping skin
Gagging
I wasn't certain what they were doing
But I had an idea
It lasted 10 minutes
Then it became silent
Did they leave
Could I leave
Silence lasts forever
Unless you think
So I thought

Have they left, have they gone
Should I stay, all night long
Here, wondering, smoldering
Deep inside my sleeping bag
Turtle in a shell
I considered what to consider
I considered schoolmates
Not from high school
But elementary
First grade, second grade
When relationships were innocent

I considered those schoolmates
First grade, second grade
I imagined most of them
Went off to college
Or were working for their parents
Butchers – Bakers – Casket Makers
Grasping legacies
Weekends off
I was happy for them
While lying in shrubs
Doing my best
To avoid getting raped
Or murdered
Those schoolmates
They had a jump on me
But something told me
And I believed it
If I could just stay alive
Make it through tonight
I might stand a chance
Of having a good run

Have they left, have they gone
I didn't budge, turtle in a shell
I considered Barry NyQuil
How we fought five times in second grade
How I was victorious on each account
Our sixth fight took place
Outside the stadium of a Twins game
In a school bus owned by a church
Without warning, Barry swung a bag
It connected with my skull
Blood gushed, ran into my eyes
Bouncing, flailing
I pinned Barry and struck his face
Repeatedly
Until religious chaperones broke us up
My gash needed stitches
His nose was broken
As people gathered
Barry claimed he won
I didn't disagree
As he opened his bag
And pulled out his secret weapon
A can of Elf Cream Soda

JARRELL - 7

It was an era when civilized people
Drank pop from glass bottles
Pepsi was king, Coke was passé
Supermarkets showed savvy
Providing canned pop for poor people
Supermarkets showed savvy
By creating their own lines
Super-Valu sold Elf
Tin cans, 12 flavors, each of which
Bore a dainty little elf
Projecting a merry expression
It was humiliating enough
Being attacked with a smirking pixie
But, if it's unavoidable
Let the victim maintain dignity
Smash their skull
With grape or orange
But never, never ever
Crown a chap with cream soda
It's undignified to all parties involved

CONVENIENCE STORE PARKING LOT

Larry and some other guy
Tossed the yellow Nerf with me
While waiting for their mutual friend
During a break in the action
They asked me to join their trio
They were heading to a lake
To meet Carrie on a pontoon
Where she would let each of them ride her
Larry said
She probably wouldn't mind a fourth
But then he cautioned me
Her boobs were different sizes
A fact that shouldn't be noted
In her presence
Because it made her self-conscious
I declined
With a manufactured reason
The other guy made a homophobic slur
Larry handed me the yellow Nerf
And went about his business

OBSERVATION

The town was quiet, the town was shy
Shy enough that it didn't go out of its way
To announce where you were
I bedded down, routine became disrupted
When I bypassed daily scriptures
In lieu of rereading RUMBLE FISH
I remembered junior high teachers
Seemed to think no boy ever read
So they coaxed us towards literature
By baiting us with THE OUTSIDERS
A fine selection, but safe, entry level
I don't know why they didn't follow up
And go the extra mile with RUMBLE FISH
It is artful
If THE OUTSIDERS was a painting
It would be *American Gothic*
Or *Whistler's Mother*
But RUMBLE FISH challenges
Pushing boundaries like Picasso
Or Francis Bacon's screaming popes
I got to thinking, and I marveled
At how brilliant S.E. Hinton was
Not just to understand the difference
But to also find a way to teach us

THREE ANGELS

First light, first ride
Three women headed to Austin
Self-proclaimed back-up singers
For Emmylou Harris
Long hair
Eyes identical
They smelled really good
Dressed modest
Almost Amish
Laura Ashley
Laura Ingalls Wilder
They loved Jesus
They liked me
They smelled really good
They sang like angels

THE SONG

They sang a song
I don't know if it was original
Or a cover, but it was beautiful
Verses were rotated, one angel at a time
But choruses were sung in unison
The last chorus
Each of the angels riffed solos
While the other two harmonized
I don't know why
I liked it as much as I did
But I did, enough in fact
When they dropped me off
I did my best to copy it
Onto the "Notes" page
In my GOOD NEWS BIBLE

FUNNY HOW PEOPLE CHANGE

V-1 Ain't it hard to live
    Ain't it hard to die
    As much as you can give
    But sometimes
    You don't even want to try
V-2 Ain't it hard to tell
    You thought you knew it well
    If you're going to heaven
    Or if there is a hell
    And what lies beyond the sky
V-3 No one thought that you would last
    They all said you'd soon be
    A part of my past
Chorus – La, La Le Da
      La, La Le Da De Da
V-4 Funny how people change
    I never thought it would happen
    This way to me
    (pause – pause – pause – pause)
    I have met . . . our God
Chorus X 12

3 A.M. AUSTIN TEXAS

I was lonely, she was pretty
Sitting across the Laundromat
Reading her satanic Bible
Short three quarters
Her final load was wet
Balancing fate with opportunity
I ponied up, she shrugged
While demonstrating a look of obligation
She took me to her car
Where she produced bottles of Dr. Pepper
Nothing was said, we drank in darkness
I was lonely, she was pretty
But, several years older, out of my league
There was nothing to lose
So I asked something pointless
To which she responded
Everyone has a season when God hates them
And leaves them to the mercy of the world
I'm pretty sure I'm having that season
I became sad and drank slowly
Realizing, our moment would be over
When the bottles were empty

THE RIVER

I was alone, I felt alone and tired
I bought a pack of cigarettes
And rested on the riverbank
When I woke, I saw an old man
And a dog, sitting uphill, we shared cigarettes
And stared across the river
I asked if this was the Bible Belt
The old man pointed to the preacher
And a group of young people
Wading into the current, wearing choir robes
First in line, a beautiful convert
She seemed excited, and nervous
Splash, the preacher dunked her
As she stood up, her face was beaming
The wet robe clung so tight
Onlooking angels blushed
The old man began to cackle
I'm not sure if he was talking to me
Or the hound, when he said
If that pretty young thing
Was in my congregation
I'd dunk her everyday

UNIVERSAL CITY

Can humans become feral, or is that just an animal thing
If humans can become feral, I'm pretty sure I might have been
Not so much because I was wild
Although there might have been some of that
But mostly because, I became intuitive
Relying heavily on instinct
Talk to anyone who has traveled the world alone
They'll tell you just how important intuition can be
At a café in Universal City, I splurged and bought breakfast
As I sopped up runny yolks with toast
I had a hunch, something pivotal was going to happen
In San Antonio
I didn't know if it would be good or bad
But if you pointed a gun at me, and made me pick
I probably would have gone with bad
After finishing two glasses of milk, the hunch didn't leave
So I did, with a feeling of uncertainty
As I stepped outside, unfolded my map of Texas
And charted a course to San Antonio

AN EXTENDED STINT IN SAN ANTONIO

Passing the city gates, I entered
And danced like David before the Lord
Proud and with purpose
Even if my purpose hadn't been made clear
When the high lowered
I wasn't sure where to go
So I followed a mob
Consisting of mostly old people
And people who looked uncertain
We approached the Alamo, I entered
Within the briefest of moments
I became underwhelmed
San Antonio was fine
If you like strip malls and white noise
I began to feel my hope was unrequited
Numbness and uncertainty
Ringing in my ears
I stopped in the middle of a generic street
And stared into the storefront window
Of a florist who displayed a bouquet

THE BOUQUET

I knew nothing about flowers
Yet I stood amazed
How wonderful they looked
I couldn't tell, or venture to guess
If they were specifically arranged
Or randomly placed into the vase
A guy walked out of the shop
And looked at me with uncertainty
I asked if he made that bouquet
He nodded yes
I asked if he had to go to school
To learn how to arrange floral patterns
He thought a spell
Before answering, before asking
If I wanted to be a florist
Respectfully, I nodded no
Staring at the flowers, smiling
And explaining
I don't know what I want to do
But I do know one thing
I want to do something
And I want to be as good at it
As you are at this

THE FOLLOWING DAY

I woke early, scouring, gathering
Collecting heaps of stones
Different sizes, shapes and colors
By noon, I had what I needed
And sorted them on asphalt
People watched
But nobody spoke
They watched, as I sorted
And laid them out on asphalt
Like a mandala or a labyrinth
But, in my mind
They were stone bouquets
As the day drew on, it occurred to me
That I could change the bouquet's colors
By spraying water on the stone
I marveled at this discovery
Until it grew dark
When I crawled into my sleeping bag
Turtle in a shell
I felt proud of the day's accomplishment
While understanding
Stone bouquets were great for a day
But longer than that . . .
Not so much

AERIAL VIEW

There is a drugstore in San Antonio
That yields easy access to its roof
It's a place of happiness
A place to thrive
The perfect space to set camp
Late at night, I stared across the street
At a gas station's vacant roof
I thought how lucky King David was
To have a rooftop
A place of happiness, a place to thrive
What I wouldn't have given
To stare across the street
And witness a Texan version of Bathsheba
Soaking, stretching, covered in suds
That could be removed with nothing more
Than a faint breeze
When the fantasy faded
A star twinkled
As they sometimes do in the movies
When something special is about to pass
I wanted to be prepared
So I broke out my Bible
And began to read

JOSHUA 6:25

But Joshua spared Rahab, the prostitute, with her family
And all who belong to her, because she hid the men
Joshua had sent as spies to Jericho . . .
And she lives among the Israelites to this day

SYNOPSIS

It's just my opinion, but . . .
Of course, lazy scholars and threatened men
Would identify Rahab as a prostitute
The Aramaic translation states she was an innkeeper
Not a brothel attendant
The Hebrew uses the term (ishah zonah)
It's really a weak phrase
But, God forbid that a woman of that era
Could be in control and lucrative
For the record . . .
It's not like I even think
Entrepreneurs are better than
Or have more value than, sex workers
I've had numerous prostitute friends
And . . . so did Jesus
But give a gal some credit
Either way, Rahab had moxie
And if I get lucky, and make it to heaven
Gosh . . . I'd love to meet her

GENESIS 6:4

The Nephilim were on the earth in those days
And also afterward, when the sons of God went to
The daughters of humans
And had children by them
These were heroes of old
Men of renown

SYNOPSIS

The Bible confuses me
Every biblical reference to an angel
Is always masculine
I'm not trying to be funny, or cute
But we know they are sexual creatures
They came to earth and did "it" with women
So were they "a"-sexual up to that point
Or homosexual
Some have mentioned that the Nephilim
Were Satan's fallen angels
Fathers to Giants
Like Goliath and the Philistines
Which brings me to another topic
Why was everyone so surprised
When David toppled Goliath
David worshipped the Living God
The Host of Host
Goliath prayed to Dagon
The Fish God
How could a God without arms and hands
Lead one to certain victory

JOHN 11:35

Jesus wept

SYNOPSIS

In addition to being the shortest verse in the Bible
Jesus wept was also inserted
By my 8th grade shop teacher
During moments when an "F" bomb
Might be considered inappropriate
In my Bible's margin, I jotted . . .
Not a cry of lamentation
Nor a wail of excessive grief
But . . .
A calm shedding of tears
I find these notes comforting
A few tears are ok
You can cry and maintain grit
But nobody, especially me
Wants to follow a blubbering Messiah

THE BOOK OF NEHEMIAH

SYNOPSIS

It's my favorite book in the Bible
A book about a clever man
A guy who knew how to network
Many people had tried to rebuild
The walls of Jerusalem
They all failed
Until Nehemiah came along
And applied elbow grease
While greasing palms of those necessary
To get the job done
Many faiths claim salvation is free
But I like works
I don't want to share my heavenly mansion
With some plop-ass who simply recites a prayer
Which leads me to another topic
I cry bullshit, do you think it was fair
When the father called for the fatted calf
And held a feast for the prodigal son
I don't, I think it was enabling as heck

1st CORINTHIANS 14:34

Woman should remain silent in church
They are not allowed to speak
But must be in submission
As the law says

SYNOPSIS

This doesn't make sense
Something is being left out
It's a douche thing to say, and Paul's not a douche
I do know Corinth was a port city
A banking capital, and home to . . .
The Goddess Aphrodite
God of fertility and subsequently, orgies
People like to follow religious concepts
Where they get laid
But Paul wasn't a pervert, he loved women
In fact, when he moved to Corinth
For 18 months, he moved into the home
Of church members, Aquila and Priscilla
He wrote them letters, doing the unthinkable
He addresses Priscilla before Aquila
Check Romans 16:3, Check Acts 18:18
Check 2nd Timothy 4:19
And if that's not enough
Check 1st Corinthians 14:34
Where his salutation starts off
Greetings Prisca and Aquila
The apostle loved them enough
To drop terms of endearment
I'm not a scripture lawyer
But I love Paul, and he loves women

THE BOOK OF REVELATIONS

SYNOPSIS

Oftentimes when your life is frantic
The Book of Revelations offers solace
When my life becomes unglued
I can't help but think
How convenient a rapture would be
The book was written by John
Many people feel John's Gospel
Was a bit oddball
Compared to Matthew, Mark and Luke's
Eventually John pissed off the Romans
And was exiled to the island of Patmos
Where he received his vision
I considered what it must be like to be exiled
The only other people I knew
Who suffered that fate
Were the Rolling Stones
When they were exiled to Main Street
Then I considered
If I would rather be exiled with John
Or Keith Richards
I couldn't decide

JOHN 18:10

Then Simon Peter, who had a sword
Drew it and struck the high priest's servant
Cutting off his right ear
(The servant's name was Malchus)

SYNOPSIS

When Christ was in the garden
And the guards came to gather him
For the crucifixion, Peter manned up
And shanked a Roman guard
The disciples were outnumbered
It was a ballsy move
Yet . . . days later when Peter was asked
Weren't you with that Christ fellow
He was alone and afraid
He denied thrice before the cock crowed
Note To Self . . .
Most of us seem to be at our best
When we are with our tribe
Cloaked in love . . .

CONCLUSION TO THE SCRIPTURES

With that, I closed my Bible
Sitting on that drugstore rooftop
Waves of loneliness crashed against my heart
While I remained sober
While I prayed for rapture
To make all of this stop
And sweep me away

THREE RIVERS

On a night that doesn't require a plan
A brick wall, a parking lot
A place to gather thoughts
A space where nothing bustles
Throw the ball, against the wall
Back into my hand
Throw the ball, against the wall
Back into my hand
By day, birds kept me calm
By night, the moon is my companion
But now . . . this moment
Throw the ball, against the wall
Back into my hand
An old man walks by, staring down
Trying to evade my glance
He's frightened
He lifts his hand
Waves a defensive salutation
I smile and wave back, knowing . . .
Some days
You just have to take what you can get

DOG - 1

Between "A" and "B"
On a road
Morning cold
Colder than expected
Between "A" and "B"
Breakfast time
Church bells chime
Bananas in Laredo
Between here and there
A large dog
A shepherd mix
Blocked my path
Looking nonplussed
Staring at my bribe
Bananas in Laredo

DOG – 2

I looked at "B"
He looked at me
Holding a stance
Daring me to pass
With no clear advantage
And everything to lose
The wisdom of mother's second husband
Whispered . . .
Avoid a kerfuffle
Dig in the duffle
More than a master
A controller of resources
A controller who understands
The power of peanut butter

DOG - 3

Stay or go
Was always the question
Offered by the road
A question without an answer
A question that reminded
Failure craves a reason
Stay or go
Was always the question
But when you have a dog
You have a friend
Why not stay
Laredo
Yesterday, today and tomorrow

DOG – 4

I didn't rub his belly
He never licked my face
But we grew close
I named him Cowboy
If you're in the company
Of a stray dog
Longer than 24 hours
You have to name it
It's the law
God's law, not mine
Cowboy didn't do tricks
Or anyone's bidding
But he slept in my camp
And in the daytime
We kept each other company
Sitting
Waiting
Neither one of us
Had a plan

DOG - 5

The park had three fountains
1000 benches surrounding a gazebo
And a small crowd
Attending a puppet show
Guy on the bench next to me
Ate pancakes
From a Styrofoam clamshell
He praised my dog
I mentioned, it wasn't my dog
He asked permission
To feed my dog pancakes
I mentioned, it wasn't my dog
He tossed pancakes in the grass
Cowboy scarfed
The guy stood to leave
And walked toward the parking lot
Cowboy looked at me, before turning
And trotting away with pancake guy
I began to feel ill

DOG - 6

Numbness, fever and regret
Jockeying for position
I considered packing up
And hitching straight through
To Corpus Christi
But I was sad and sweaty
My skin was sticky
So I headed to camp
Crawled inside my sleeping bag
Turtle in a shell
I was sad and sweaty
I considered this
I considered that
Before reaching the conclusion
Nothing good would happen today
So I rested, motionless
For hours, realizing
I'd pull out in the morning
Get an early start
Eat breakfast
Bananas in Laredo

ANOTHER WHITE VAN

At first glance, the van gave comfort
It was an industrial van, filled with this and that
Filled with items that might roll about
If a quick turn had been made
The driver was a kind man, a man to be trusted
In a world that seldom allowed this luxury
He stared ahead as he drove
He offered no advice
The van pulled into a parking lot
Of the place where he worked
I said thanks for the ride
He paused, considered, and finally offered . . .
You've only got 90 minutes to Corpus
I'd take you, but I have meetings
Let's grab a driver
And get you where you need to be
It was hard to contain my smile
As we crossed the threshold, he disappeared
Several women in the foyer
Stopped playing a piano
Just long enough to examine me
Just long enough to realize
I didn't offer anything
More exciting than their music

END OF THE ROAD

My driver was a big man
Bear paws on the steering wheel
And roars of laughter
When I confessed to some of my shortcomings
My driver was a kind man
Calm in the midst of crisis
Using strategic silence
To frame a hope he had for me
As we hit the end of the line
He explained matter-of-fact
Years from now, you'll laugh about this
Or . . . you'll be dead, and it won't matter
Stay off the water at night
Then he handed me a present from his boss
A bag containing $50 and a 6-pack of Bud
Lightning shot through my body
I got dizzy, I sat down
Once I realized
There was no more country left to cross

TIRED

I wasn't sure where to go, the sun glared
People along the water
It had to be midday; my eyes grew heavy
Hurry, scurry
Groups of people, groups of mobs
I wasn't sure where to rest
I couldn't figure out why I was so tired
Spent, hollow and sad
Laying on concrete
Outside the Memorial Coliseum
Laying in the slipstream
Of a bustle that was foreign to me
Boys my age laughed, swore
And played hacky sack
As I drifted off
Spent, hollow and sad

THE MESSAGE

I had no idea where I was
When I woke
The noise had reduced, the crowd thinned out
I was hungry, thirsty, needed a restroom
But I was disoriented, I couldn't figure out
Which necessity should be tackled first
I sat up and gently rocked
I sat up and stared forward
At nothing particular
Until *hark* what did I behold . . .
A paneled station wagon cruising
Cruising until it stopped, in front of me
The driver was alone
He could have been Morgan Freeman's brother
He asked if I was ok
Defensively, I remained silent
The man seemed to understand, he nodded
Before offering . . . I don't mean to pry son
But you need to call home, today
Then with a look of indifference
He left me alone, to wonder

ALONG THE WATERFRONT

I wondered, I actually wondered
If the guy was a crackpot, or an angel
I wondered, I hate to admit
If I was a crackpot, or a demon
I dragged my gear
I saw a payphone
I tried to subdue the urge
To call home
But conveniently for me
That's about the same time
I determined the man in the station wagon
Had to be an angel

RING - RING

A call was placed, the charges were reversed
And accepted
Ma, it's me . . .
Tick-Tock, silence dragged
Ma, it's me
She cried, silence dragged
Neither of us knew how to proceed
She announced
She had booted her second husband
She announced next autumn
Winter at the latest
She would be selling the house
And moving to India
I was told I could return
Live rent-free and get a job
So I could prepare a bankroll
Before being pushed from the nest
I asked if the cops had been around
To which she replied
That's your business, not mine
Then she hung up
When she hung up
I gathered my belongings
And started home

UPON MY ARRIVAL

My homecoming was met without ceremony
Our woes were not discussed
We watched TV and ate Chinese takeout
Our relationship was not discussed
It's hard to focus on a loved one
When you've lost touch with yourself
An outcome, both of us were experiencing
Each day mother discarded possessions
The house was nearly empty
Polite conversations echoed
The tone seemed unnatural
Nights passed slowly
As mother thought about her second husband
I wondered if the cops would grab me
Emptiness, echoes, loneliness, uncertainty
A new reality
One neither of us would volunteer for
However, together . . .
Our struggle seemed doable

EMERGING SON - 1

I enrolled in baking school
Set to start the following year
In the meantime, I got a job
Working third shift
As an orderly
On a security floor
Where most of the residents
Came from prisons or asylums
With Alzheimer's or some kind of dementia
That had reached a point
Where it was no longer safe
For them to be
In general population

FADING MOTHER - 1

She put the house up for sale

EMERGING SON - 2

At night, when I started my shift
Many of the aggressive residents
Had a mesh vest called a Houdini posey
Slid over their torso
The vest had straps which were tied
Underneath the bed frame
Or onto the bedrails

FADING MOTHER- 2

She got a passport

EMERGING SON - 3

Even though it was against the rules
Sometimes the orderlies
Had to wrestle residents
And force meds on them
Oftentimes combative residents
Were twice the size
Of an average-sized nurse
This breach of protocol was justified
Because the end result
Was in everybody's best interest

FADING MOTHER - 3

She received required vaccinations

EMERGING SON - 4

I seemed to have a knack
And could predict
When residents would die
Sometimes their fate was obvious
Other times, not so much
But I had a knack
And the third shift charge nurse
Realized this
And assigned me
To take care of individuals
Who were about to expire

FADING MOTHER – 4

She had the downstairs shower fixed

EMERGING SON - 5

I checked out apartments in St. Paul

VANISHING MOTHER - 5

Mother looked calm
So calm, it was alarming
But good

EMERGING SON - 6

I decided I wanted to get married
I was determined

BON VOYAGE

The day I moved
Everything I owned fit into a Toyota
When I said goodbye to mother
I said it as if we would talk soon
When the reality was
I had no idea when I would see her again
We stood in her kitchen
Looking at each other
She smoked a cigarette
I just stood there
Arms hanging, rocking side to side
She didn't know what to say either
Neither one of us had a clue
What would become our new normal
As I reached for the door
I asked . . . are you scared
She said nah . . . are you
I smiled without answering
Because I no longer
Wanted to lie

SIX MONTHS LATER...

ANOTHER DILEMMA

I found a woman who agreed to marry me
She lived in a small town
She told me she would move to St. Paul
If I got an apartment on Grand Ave.
She told me she would agree to marry me
If I quit smoking
I agreed, but I continued smoking
Most nights, I lit my cigs with a candle
One night I bumped the candle
Wax sprayed
And soaked into my designer shag carpet
I panicked, how would I explain this
To a wife who was suspicious and smart
Mother was out of touch
I didn't know who to call
So, I called the library
When I discussed my dilemma with the librarian
She told me to place a moist cloth over the wax
And run a hot iron over it
This seemed like a great idea
But . . . I didn't have an iron

CRYSTAL SHOPPING CENTER

On the day I had to return
To my former neighborhood
To pick up my G.E.D. certificate
I cruised across my former stomping grounds
When I passed by Target
(Years before it became Super Target)
I remembered my carpet
I remembered the wax and my future wife
Circumstance influenced me
To pull in and purchase an iron
As I crossed the threshold
It felt different
I had been in this store
Hundreds of times
But . . . this was the first time
I entered as an adult

AISLE #8

I looked at this, I looked at that
I looked for nothing in particular
But I relished the feeling
Of walking this familiar territory
With an elevated maturity
Eventually, I found irons
Examined them, selected the cheapest
And marched toward the check-out
I stood in line behind a woman
Making a purchase
Consisting of many items
I had time, there was no hurry
I had time, the woman rifled coupons
Until she looked up, and back at me
It was the Pop Bottle Lady
My natural reaction was to turn away
But her stare locked me down
Time froze, things exploded inside me
I began crumbling
My body began to shake
I had no idea what was happening
I didn't know what to do

AISLE #8

She just stood there
She continued staring
Finally, the dam broke
I started to cry
Tears gushed
Tears allocated for the Pop Bottle Lady
And for every other thing
I had been able to block out
Over the course of my young life
Cashiers on adjacent registers
Customers in other aisles
They stared at me with confusion
But somehow, I made it
I did it
I passed through shame's gauntlet
Apologizing . . .
I'm sorry, I'm sorry
I'm sorry

AISLE #8

Pop Bottle Lady moved forward
Reached out her hand
And placed it on my forearm
Her eyes shined, she was happy
Her hand gripped with authority
Her smile widened
I might have been hyperventilating
As she explained
Of course, I forgive you
I am proud of you
You are a good man . . .
Then she let go
Finished her transaction
And left without further incident
Normality resumed
Our moment . . . my moment
Was tabled quickly
As customers exited their lanes

TARGET PARKING LOT

After tossing my iron in the back seat
I hopped into my Toyota
Kids in America by Kim Wilde
Was playing on the radio
A song I usually welcomed gladly
But on this afternoon, I just sat
Quietly, thinking of nothing
But thinking, waiting for a thought to stick
After shock washed away, reality hit
I was mortified by my display of emotion
But then I thought about the Pop Bottle Lady
And her eyes, she more than forgave me
She expressed something
I wasn't equipped to understand
Then . . . hollowness filled me, not in a bad way
But a hollowness that purged
It was that moment I realized
If sitting in humiliation is necessary
To lift melancholy
It's a small price to pay

A FINAL THOUGHT

When I think of Texas
I remember big sky and open spaces
Rattlesnakes at sunset
Enjoying the asphalt's warmth
When I think of Texas
I remember hitchhiking and freeways
Truck stops and rest stops
Packed with hookers and Christians
Demonstrating equal enthusiasm
Denton, Dallas, Austin
Corpus Christi too
Mile after mile of on-ramps and off-ramps
Where roadhouses were filled with women
Who believed men in black hats
Gave guardian angels purpose
When I think of Texas
I remember setting camp under bridges
Praying the moon would vanish
So the world would become dark enough
To dream of Minnesota

THE END

BOOK CLUB QUESTIONS

1. Boy's journey took place in an era without technology. Could a similar trip ever happen today? Should it?

2. What are some examples of Boy's resourcefulness?

3. Boy's story offers an unvarnished look at loneliness. Talk about the instances which you remember most clearly.

4. Discuss the impact of the Pop Bottle Lady on Boy.

5. There are many spiritual elements to Boy's journey. What were they and what was their effect on him?

6. Boy's trip from Minnesota to Texas was an extreme example of a life-changing decision. Have you ever made a similar decision that challenged you?

7. Name some examples of occasions when Boy experienced kindness from strangers.

8. Were you surprised about Boy's decision to marry when he returned? Why or why not?

BEHIND THE SCENES

Many years ago, I was fortunate enough to attract the attention of the Duchess, St. Paul's Poet Laureate. She insisted that I join her, a judge, and a proofreader, to share our work and encourage one another.

My colleagues presented pieces that were pristine and well thought-out.

I brought a poem called ... 3 a.m. Austin Texas.

Duchess loved it, but I quickly became embarrassed.

I didn't believe my work held up to my companions.

On my ensuing visits I brought love poems, poems with clever word play, very much wanting my ideas to appear more civil.

After several months, Duchess told me in private that I was missing the mark. She said the biggest advantage I had over other writers was ... I was me.

Years passed before I understood, before I really believed my mentor's advice.

So I started working on this book and about the time it was halfway done ...

The pandemic hit and Duchess died isolated in a care facility.

Carol Connolly ...

I know it's late in coming, but I hope somehow, the Goddess will let you see this book.

I will always love you the most ...

Klecko

Bio

Eventually, Boy grew up to become an internationally acclaimed baker and award-winning poet. He currently spends his time in the company of origami cranes and empty whiskey bottles.

CPSIA information can be obtained
at www.ICGtesting.com
Printed in the USA
BVHW070722020921
615857BV00006B/33

9 780578 957067